Violin Exam Pieces

ABRSM Grade 1

Selected from the 2016–2019 syllabus

Name

Date of exam

Contents

Violin consultant: Philippa Bunting
Footnotes: Edward Huws Jones (EHJ) and Anthony Burton

Other pieces for Grade 1

First published in 2015 by ABRSM (Publishing) Ltd, a wholly owned subsidiary of ABRSM, 24 Portland Place, London W1B 1LU, United Kingdom © 2015 by The Associated Board of the Royal Schools of Music

Music origination by Andrew Jones Cover by Kate Benjamin & Andy Potts Printed in England by Caligraving Ltd, Thetford, Norfolk

A:1

L'homme armé

Arranged by Edward Huws Jones

Anon.

L'homme armé The Armed Man

L'homme armé was a well-known French folk song of the 15th century and many composers of the period, such as Dufay, wove it into their church music. The tune has become popular again with composers of our own time, including Peter Maxwell Davies and Karl Jenkins. The identity of the 'armed man' is a mystery. Some think he was the Archangel Michael; others link him to the military turmoil of the period. Look out for the key signature! The piece is in the Dorian mode starting on E, which is like E minor but with a C♯. EHJ

Minuet

BWV Anh. II 116

from *Clavierbüchlein vor Anna Magdalena Bach*, 1725

A:2

Arranged by Mary Cohen

Anon.

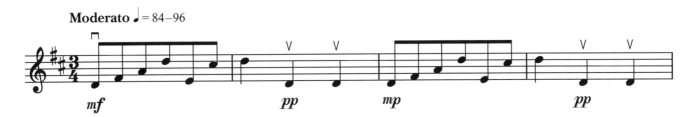

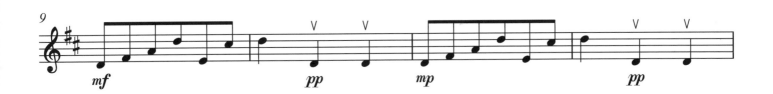

Clavierbüchlein Little Keyboard Book

The minuet is a dance of French origin which was popular in the 18th century. This is an adaptation of the first section of a minuet, for harpsichord or clavichord, included in the *Little Keyboard Book for Anna Magdalena Bach* of 1725, a manuscript copied by the famous German composer Johann Sebastian Bach and members of his family for Bach's second wife Anna Magdalena. The piece is usually said to be by Bach himself, but in the standard catalogue of his music it is included in the appendix (*Anhang*), as it does not bear his name and may well be by another composer. Although the original metronome mark is ♩ = 84–96, a slightly faster tempo of ♩ = *c.*104 would be acceptable in the exam.

AB 3779

Écossaise

WoO 86

Arranged by Sheila Nelson

Ludwig van Beethoven
(1770–1827)

'Écossaise' is the French word for 'Scottish', and was applied in the 19th century to a type of dance in quick 2/4 time which was thought to be of Scottish origin. On 14 November 1825, Beethoven produced his very last compositions for solo piano: a waltz and an écossaise, to be included in two albums of dance music published in Vienna for use at carnival time. Because the écossaise was published in a collection, it was not given a separate opus number: hence its inclusion in the list of his 'WoO', which stands for *Werke ohne Opuszahl*, German for 'works without opus number'. It is presented here in an adaptation for violin and piano.

The Grey Dove

B:1

Arranged by Paul de Keyser and Fanny Waterman

I. M. Komorowski
(1824–57)

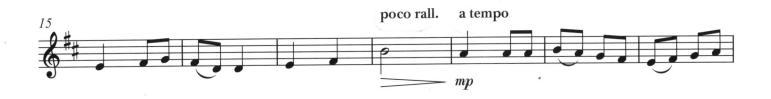

Ignacy Komorowski (sometimes spelt Komarovsky) was a Polish composer, a few years younger and even more short-lived than his compatriot Chopin. He was best known for his songs, which often used Polish folk idioms. This one is in a lively dance rhythm, and although the melody seems to be in D major it actually ends, in the manner of a modal folk song, on B. In the second verse (from b. 19) the melody is initially presented as a canon between the violin and the right-hand piano part.

Greek Wedding

Arranged by Edward Huws Jones

Trad. Greek

This traditional Greek wedding song, originally called 'Tou Gamou', has been arranged by Edward Huws Jones, a composer, arranger and violinist who specializes in folk music. He suggests: 'Imagine you are part of a Greek band playing for a wedding party, accompanied by accordion and double bass – and in the pizzicato bars you can even join in with the bouzouki! Then when you get to the *forte* in b. 17 you can really play out and enjoy using lots of bow.'

Pitlochry

No. 15 from *The Microjazz Violin Collection 1*

B:3

Christopher Norton
(born 1953)

Christopher Norton was born in New Zealand, but moved to Britain to study at the University of York. Active as a composer, educationist and record producer, he is best known for his *Microjazz* series of pieces in popular styles for various instruments. His 'Pitlochry' is named after a town, popular with tourists, in central Scotland. The melody includes 'Scotch snap' (*short*–long) rhythms, and the piano accompaniment suggests the drone of the bagpipes. Although the original metronome mark is ♩ = *c*.88–92, a more relaxed tempo of ♩ = *c*.84 would be acceptable in the exam.

Stoppin' off in Louisiana

No. 2 from *Violin Globetrotters*

(easier version)

Ros Stephen
(born 1972)

Ros Stephen is a violinist, composer and teacher based in Bristol, in the west of England. Her *Violin Globetrotters* is a collection of pieces in traditional styles from different parts of the world. 'Stoppin' off in Louisiana' is in the style of a Cajun two-step. Cajuns, French-speaking people who live mostly in the state of Louisiana in the south of the USA, have a lively tradition of folk music played on fiddles and accordion; the Cajun two-step, Ros Stephen explains, is 'great music for dancing'.

The Muppet Show Theme

C:2

Arranged by David Blackwell

Jim Henson (1936–90) and
Sam Pottle (1934–78)

It's time to play the music,
It's time to light the lights.
It's time to meet the Muppets on *The Muppet Show* tonight.

The Muppet Show was a much-loved television puppet series produced in Britain between 1976 and 1981 for transmission in Britain and the USA. (Many of its puppeteers also worked on the long-running American series *Sesame Street*.) It took the form of a variety show presented in a theatre, featuring various animal and human puppets and a genuinely human guest star. This theme, in different versions, opened and closed each episode. It was jointly written by the American puppeteer Jim Henson, who created and produced the series, and the American composer and musical director Sam Pottle.

Elenke

Arranged by Polly Waterfield

Trad. Bulgarian

This piece is taken from a collection called *Gypsy Jazz*, which the editors, Polly Waterfield and Timothy Kraemer, describe as 'an invitation to a musical journey', giving players an opportunity 'to travel horizons beyond "classical" music and there discover a world of traditional songs and dances'. 'Elenke' is a folk song from Bulgaria which should be played like a dance, because it is about dancing. The editors summarize its story: 'Elenke is called to her lover's sick-bed but she refuses to go: "I won't leave this merry dancing for a moment. Dancing makes me happy!"'

© 1996 by Faber Music Ltd, London WC1B 3DA
Reproduced from *Gypsy Jazz – Easy Level* by permission of the publishers. All rights reserved. All enquiries about this piece, apart from those directly relating to the exams, should be addressed to Faber Music Ltd, Bloomsbury House, 74–77 Great Russell Street, London WC1B 3DA.